MW00843977

WATERH●LE

A Guide To Digging Your Own Well

by Bob Mellin

Balboa Publishing

San Anselmo, CA

All rights reserved. No part of this book may be reproduced in any form or by any means, electronic or mechanical, including photocopying, recording or by any information storage and retrieval system without written permission from the author or publisher, except for the inclusion of brief quotations in a review.

The development of this guide was based on the experience and knowledge of the author with input from the numerous resources noted in the acknowledgements, appendix and bibliography. The information contained herein is true and complete to the best of the author's knowledge and is not intended to promote the violation of any laws or statutes.

The author and publisher disclaim any and all liability incurred because of the use of information contained in this guide.

Wholesale rates available to Water Districts, Government Agencies and the trade.

© 1991, Robert A. Mellin, Jr.

First Edition

10 9 8 7 6 5 4 3 2 1

Printed in the United States of America

**Library of Congress
Cataloging in Publication Data**
Mellin, Robert A., Jr.

WATERHOLE
A Guide To Digging Your Own Well

Library of Congress Catalog Card No.: 91-072454
ISBN 0-935902-21-X Paperback

Cover Illustration: Martha Weston
Illustrations & Photography: Bob Mellin
Design & Typography: Sharon Nielsen

Published by:
        Balboa Publishing
        11 Library Place
        San Anselmo, CA 94960
        (415) 453-8886

To
Mom & Dad

ACKNOWLEDGEMENTS

The author appreciates the support and information provided by the following:

David Baldwin, The Natural Gardening Company.

Ray Forster, Manager, Forster Pump & Engineering, Inc.

Robert B. Lerios, Water Engineering Technician, Forster Pump & Engineering, Inc.

Arthur M. Marthinsen, Marin County Environmental Health Services, Department of Health and Human Services.

Haley and Joseph Mellin, Balboa Publishing Corporation.

Sharon Nielsen, Production Manager, Nielsen Graphics.

Peter Reimuller, President, California Tank Distributors.

Daniel Rosenthal, President, DanArt Corporation.

Betty Swatsenbarg, Surface and Ground Water Data Section, California Department of Water Resources.

Mike Whyte, Manager, Booksmith, Inc.

Nothing in this world can take the place of persistence. Talent will not; nothing is more common than unsuccessful men with talent. Genius will not; unrewarded genius is almost a proverb. Education will not; the world is full of educated derelicts. Persistence and determination alone are omnipotent. The slogan "press on" has solved and always will solve the problems of the human race.

CALVIN COOLIDGE

TABLE OF CONTENTS

READ THIS FIRST

There are over 13 million domestic wells in the United States. More than 50 million Americans obtain their drinking water from individual home supply wells. Every day hundreds of people dig their own wells.

Most do it the right way, and create a safe, productive source of water. Some do it the wrong way and create a problem that can be very expensive and can contaminate the ground water supply for their entire community. This book is a guide to digging your own well the right way.

This is not a comprehensive collection of everything there is to know about digging wells. Rather, this book contains enough information to get the job done correctly, and inexpensively. See the bibliography if you want more information on any of the component steps in digging a well.

From the beginning, you should understand the importance of protecting the purity of the ground water you plan to tap. Regulations regarding well digging vary depending on location. Some states have no restrictions, other areas have precise guidelines.

Before digging your own well, you should find out what regulations or ordinances exist in your area. You should also read this entire book. Be aware of all the issues and steps involved before getting started.

Digging a well is like anything worthwhile – not easy, but worth the effort. The process of planning and creating your own water source is as satisfying as the water you produce.

Enjoy the process while it lasts. Don't rush it. Work on it a little at a time — a couple hours each day. Like whittling or painting a picture — work on it when you need the therapy. In between times, tell everyone who'll listen how its going. Mention what layers of sediment you've struck, how deep you are, etc. They'll get real tired of hearing about your well, but you'll enjoy it.

This book is intended to help you make informed decisions about digging a well. It provides an overview of some of the methods, costs, benefits, and legal and environmental issues. If you're going to dig a well — do it right.

Don't worry about whether or not you're digging in the right spot. You'll either hit water or you won't. Either way you'll have had a great experience and you'll be able to stop wondering whether there's water there or not. The fact that you're reading this book means that you've got a gut-level curiosity about what it would be like to dig your own well. So go for it!

Digging your own well is one of the most satisfying projects you'll ever undertake. It doesn't require much in the way of skill or expensive tools. Just some thorough planning and methodical execution. And with a little luck you will have a productive well you can enjoy for years.

But enough pep talk. Read the rest of this book, then get your tools and supplies together and start digging.

Remember - ENJOY THE PROCESS! You'll be finished all too soon.

Wishing you well,   *Bob Mellin*

AN OVERVIEW

This guide discusses these eight areas involved in digging your own well:

1. Environmental Impact Considerations

2. Planning and Preparation

3. Digging the Well

4. Installing the Well Casing

5. Sealing the Casing

6. Installing the Pump

7. Disinfecting, Use and Maintenance

8. Abandonment

WHAT'S A WELL?

The California Water Code[1] defines a well or water well as:
". . . any artificial excavation constructed by any method for the purpose of extracting water from . . . the underground."

The ground acts like a sponge in holding water. Water is stored, and in some cases flows, in layers of permeable rock, sand and/or gravel below the surface called aquifers. How far below the surface is important to you. You'll only be able to dig about 25 to 30 feet by hand. If you have to go deeper, some kind of power equipment will be needed.

The aquifer below your property is also referred to as the "water table." The level and flow of this water source can rise and fall depending on rainfall, soil conditions, and other factors you usually can't control.

It is important how quickly the well refills itself as water is drawn from it. This is called the well's recovery rate and depends on many things like the density of the soil and the subterranean water supply. At first, water will seep in through the well's sides in little droplets. As water is removed from the well, water veins develop which lead to the point of least resistance: your well. Continuing to use your well further develops these streams and will help improve the well's recovery rate to its maximum.

---

[1] Sec. 13710 California Water Code.

TOPSOIL

WATER-BEARING
SAND AND GRAVEL

CLAY

ENVIRONMENTAL IMPACT

Pay attention to this section, so your well won't damage the environment and become a very EXPENSIVE problem.

The primary concern is that you will contaminate the ground water. That is bad for you and everyone around you. And if you do contaminate the groundwater, you can be fined heavily. That, too, is bad.

So take a few simple precautions and you won't have any problems:

1. Check your local regulations regarding well drilling and operation. Some communities require permits and inspections. Some even tax wells and restrict how much you can pump from them. Some areas have no legal restrictions at all.

For instance, in many parts of California, "No person shall dig ... a well that may intersect ground water without first applying for and receiving a permit ..."[1]

The penalty for failure to obtain a permit before commencing work for which a permit is required, if subsequently granted a permit for this work, is to pay double the standard permit fee.

---

[1] California Model Well Standards Ordinance, Water Code Sec. 13801.

Where permits are required, the permit fee ranges from zero to $400. or more. See the Appendix for references and agencies to contact for environmental impact information. Find out in advance so you won't be sorry later.

2. Keep stuff out of the well that doesn't belong in it. This includes:

□ surface runoff
□ foreign matter and liquids
□ anything else

Once you start digging, keep contaminants (just about anything) away from the hole. Keep the well covered between digging sessions.

3. Consider whether you may be digging into something you shouldn't, like utility lines, burial grounds, toxic waste dumps, etc. Check with authorities if you have any doubts.

4. Install a concrete seal around the top 10 feet of the casing to prevent surface water from seeping into the well. The casing should extend at least 12 inches above the surface.

5. Keep the finished well covered and secure so no contaminants can find their way into the well.

6. Besides not putting things in the well that don't belong there, it's equally important not to take things out of the well that are hazardous – like sewage! If you dig a well too close to a sewer main (within 50 feet) or lateral sewer line leading to your house (within 50 feet for clay, 25 feet for cast iron or plastic), you may tap into water contaminated by a leaky sewer line. If you have any doubts, check with your local sanitary district for sewer line locations before you dig.

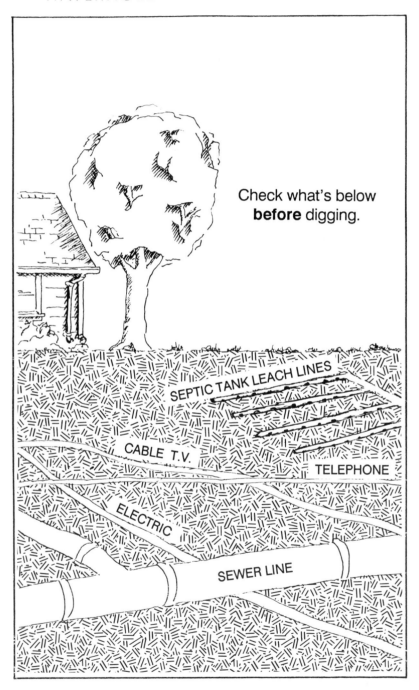

Check what's below **before** digging.

If you are considering drinking the water from your well, have it tested by a qualified laboratory service (see Appendix) to make sure it is suitable for human consumption. Studies[2] performed by the Environmental Protection Agency have shown bacterial (coliform) contamination in as many as 40% of the ground water wells sampled. Don't take the bacterial purity of your water for granted!

The studies showed the following deficiencies in well construction to affect the bacterial safety of the water supply:

- insufficient and substandard well-casing
- inadequate "formation seal" between the casing and the bore hole
- poor joining of casing joints
- lack of sanitary covers
- use of well pits to protect from freezing

Any of these deficiencies may allow bacterial contamination from the surface to reach the ground water. Each will be avoided in the directions presented in this guide.

---

[2] EPA - 570/9-75 001 Manual of Water Well Construction.

TOOLS & MATERIALS

You'll need some tools and materials to dig, case and seal a 25 foot well:

TOOLS

- □ auger
- □ circular saw
- □ digging bar
- □ hand saw
- □ (2) pipe wrenches
- □ coarse sandpaper
- □ shovel
- □ 30 feet of ¼-inch rope
- □ wheelbarrow

Optional

- □ gloves
- □ post hole digger
- □ hand trowel

MATERIALS

Auger extensions:

- ☐ (1) 2-foot length of 3/4" galvanized pipe
- ☐ (6) 4-foot lengths of 3/4" galvanized pipe
- ☐ (7) 3/4" galvanized couplings

Well lining (casing):

- ☐ 30 feet of 4" **Schedule 40** PVC pipe
- ☐ (2) 4" PVC pipe caps
- ☐ PVC purple primer
- ☐ PVC glue
- ☐ (6) 80 lb. bags of pea gravel
- ☐ (9) 90# bags of concrete mix

Other:

- ☐ Collar - 5 gallon bucket with bottom cut out
- ☐ Temporary well covering - 3' x 3' plywood scrap
- ☐ pump and feeder pipe (see section on The Pump)
- ☐ 10-foot measuring stick
- ☐ scrap lumber for framing pad for pump.
- ☐ (2) 3-inch hose clamps
- ☐ 40 feet of string with weight at end

Adjustable auger   Fixed auger

COST

Assuming you've got a few common tools, here's an estimate of what it will cost you to install your own 25-foot well:

Tools

      Hand Auger $48.

Materials

Auger extensions:
      (1) 2-foot length of 3/4" galv. pipe   3.
      (6) 4-foot lengths of 3/4" galv. pipe   26.
      (7) 3/4" galv. couplings   6.

Casing and seal:
      30 feet of 4" Schedule 40 PVC   80.
      (2) 4" Schedule 40 PVC caps   20.
      (1) 4" Schedule 40 PVC coupling   5.
      (9) 90-pound bags of pea gravel   36.
      (6) 80-pound bags of pea gravel   15

Equipment

      Pump $40. to $350.

Other

      Permit (if required) $80. to $380.

BENEFITS

What are the benefits of digging your own well?

Well, what's your monthly water bill?

On average, most people use between 50 and 80 percent[1] of their water on their yard. And most of that (60 to 80 percent) is for lawns.

So even if you plan to use your well water for landscape watering only, the impact on your water expense should be significant. Assuming you can cut your water bill in half by using your well for all of your landscape watering needs, it shouldn't be difficult to figure out how long it will take for the well to pay for itself.

As mentioned earlier, more than 50 million Americans obtain their water from their own ground water wells[2]. So if you have your own well, you've got a lot of company.

Besides the financial, the personal benefits can be considerable. Digging your own well will supply you with an almost endless source of entertaining well-digging stories to share with your family and friends. And you'll notice a boost in your self-esteem — sort of like laying your own linoleum.

---

[1] Report #34, University of California, 1976.

[2] EPA - 570/9-75-001, Manual of Well Construction Practices.

Household Water Requirements

Use	Gallons
Full bathtub	30
Full wash basin	2
Flushed toilet	5
Average shower	25
Dishwasher	18
Clothes washer	36
Lawn Watering	**500**
Milk cow per day	35
Horse per day	10
Sheep/Goat per day	2

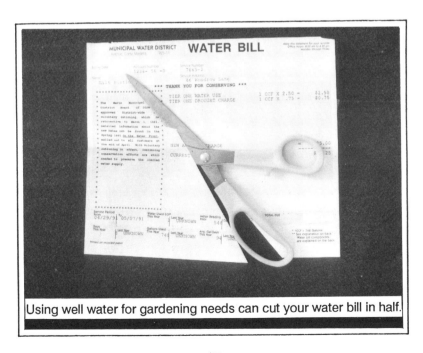

Using well water for gardening needs can cut your water bill in half.

PICKING THE SPOT

You could get rich if you knew where to dig for water. There are lots of stories about different ways to find water but the process remains part luck, part skill. You may want to begin by using a Y-shaped stick (divining rod) and dowsing for water like they do in the movies. This doesn't work but it makes a good story.

It's best to use some common sense. If you live at the top of a mountain, you've got a poor chance of digging a successful well. If you live on the flood plains in a valley, you've got a very good chance of digging a successful well. If you live somewhere in between, your chances are somewhere in between.

Ask around in your neighborhood. Do any neighbors have wells? How deep are their wells? How much do their wells produce? Do their wells dry up in the summer?

For a hand-augered well, it's about as much work testing for water as it is to go ahead and dig the well. Decide whether or not there is a good chance you'll hit water and then go for it!

As for the exact spot in your yard, its sort of like looking for a parking place at the mall. Why not look right in front of the store you want to shop at first? Why not drill at the spot in your yard you'd like your well to be?

Poor site for a well.

Good site for a well.

The spot should have as much clearance around it as possible. Overhead wires and tree limbs are bad. Take the necessary precautions described in the Environmental Impact section so you won't be digging into utility lines, sewer pipes, leach fields, etc. And don't dig where there's lots of foot traffic since you don't want people "playing" with your well.

Also, you should consider the possibility of bringing in more equipment to drill with if you don't reach water on your own. If you dig as far as you can and don't reach water, you may wish to call in a company that uses, say, a hydraulic drill. Some of these rigs are mounted on the back of a truck and some come broken down to be assembled on your property. In either case, access to the well site should be a consideration in choosing the spot.

If it turns up dry or too rocky, you may have to move it. But dig first where you would like the well to be.

You may want to have a little ground-breaking ceremony with pictures, ribbon cutting, cake, etc. Or, then again, you may not.

Some people like to mark the spot with an "X".

PREPARING THE SITE

It's a good idea to clean up the drill site and give yourself as much space as possible before you start digging. Overhead obstructions will get in the way and can be a serious hazard.

Clean away all debris, vegetation, loose rocks, etc. in a 10-foot circle around the spot you've picked. Anything you leave around the drill hole will find its way into the hole and that's not good. Take some time to clean the drill site at the beginning - you'll be glad you did.

If you use a hand auger, you should anticipate that it will eventually get quite long, and relatively heavy, before you are through. When you withdraw a long auger from the hole, you'll need a path to lay it down on to empty the bucket. So you might as well start by clearing a path from the hole about twenty feet long and four feet wide.

When the site is clear, dig a hole at "the spot" 1 or 2 feet deep (use a post hole digger if you have one) and fill it with water. When the water disappears, fill it again. Repeat this to pre-soften the soil.

At this time you can install a "collar" at the hole if you have one. This can be a 5-gallon bucket or plastic nursery pot with the bottom removed. The collar will keep loose soil and diggings from jumping into the hole as you work. The idea is to avoid digging the same dirt out of the hole twice.

A "collar" can be made out of a 5-gallon bucket.

Pre-soaking the spot makes digging easier.

DIGGING THE WELL

There are many methods of well construction available:

Boring - with hand or power auger
Digging - with hand or power tool
Driving - forcing a pointed casing
Jetting - jet drill percussion/pressure pump
Cable Tool - lifting/dropping drilling tools
Rotary Drill - rotating drill pipe and bit
Reverse Circulation - fluid forced down
Air Rotary - air forced rotary drilling
Down-the-hole - pneumatic bottom hole drill

As you might guess, a different method is best for each different situation. The "boring" method using a hand auger is the method described in this guide and is ideal for digging a "shallow" (up to 30-feet deep) well. It is the least expensive and one of the few that can be done by hand.

If you've soaked the ground as suggested, it should be fairly soft for the first 8 to 10 feet. You may wish to use a clamshell type post hole digger for the first 3 or 4 feet but it's not necessary. Don't make the top of the hole any larger than necessary (match the diameter of the "collar" you install). Remember, you'll be sealing the top of whatever hole you dig with concrete so don't make it too wide.

21

A post hole digger may be used for the first 3 or 4 feet.

The "collar" keeps material from falling into the well.

Use the auger by turning it in a slow, steady motion, and its blades will draw it into the ground. When the auger bucket fills up, pull it up out of the hole slowly and carefully and empty it.

Until you hit clay or other material that will stick to the auger, you can empty it simply by turning it on its side and letting the soil fall out. To remove clay or other material that is stuck to the bucket, a hand trowel is useful, as is an elevated surface to knock the auger against. A 2-foot high 2"×4" stuck in the ground works well for this.

If you can feel the auger encountering rocks, it can help to reverse direction briefly. Working the teeth of the auger back and forth in this manner frequently loosens embedded rocks.

Depending on soil conditions, a digging bar (approx. 2" diameter steel bar about 5 to 7 feet long weighing about 40 lbs.) will be helpful if you encounter rocks. By dropping the bar into the hole, rocks in your path normally break loose so you can remove them with the auger.

Once you've dug beyond the digging bar's length, you'll have to attach a rope to the end of the bar to retrieve it after dropping it into the well. Attach the rope securely to the bar (two hose clamps work well) so you don't lose the bar in the well.

If you are unlucky enough to strike a rock that's just too big to crack or remove, you have several options:

1. move the well
2. get a more powerful drill
3. dynamite

Empty the auger against a vertical 2"×4".

Attach a rope to the digging bar with two hose clamps.

Try moving the well over 4 or 5 feet and begin again. Your bore hole should be plumb and not curve off at an angle; trying to dig around a rock is a **bad** idea. If you've dug onto a single, big rock, moving over a few feet and starting over should solve the problem. If you've encountered a broad layer of rock, moving the hole a few feet probably won't help. In this case you might want to consider hiring a professional drilling company to use more powerful equipment to penetrate the obstacle.

See the section on Abandonment if you quit on a hole. Properly sealing an unsuccessful hole is important since it is now a possible point of entry for contaminants into the water table. It may also affect the purity the well at your new digging location.

If you accidentally drop something into the hole, the auger is usually the best tool to use to remove it. If you've dropped something like a pipewrench or a glove, just keep drilling and the auger will "collect" the item.

If something like the digging bar is dropped into the well, you'll have to snag it with a weighted rope which, with a little luck, you can wind around the object and slowly pull it free.

As you drill deeper, you'll notice the auger disappearing into the ground. When its handle gets so low you can no longer turn it, its time to add an extension pipe to the auger.

The first extension you add should be a 2-foot length. Add it directly above the auger bucket and leave it in this position as you add later lengths of pipe. As the auger gets longer, heavier and more slippery, you'll be able to grab the coupling at this 2-foot point and keep the auger from slipping out of your hands.

BIG ROCK
(Time to move.)

ADDING EXTENSION PIPES TO AUGER

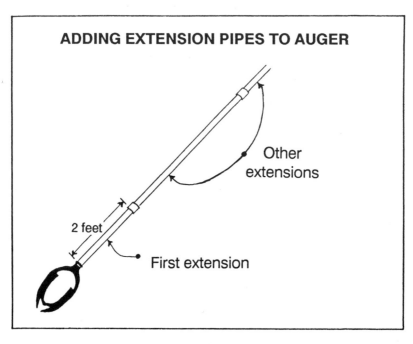

Other
extensions

2 feet

First extension

————— Adding Extensions to the Auger —————

Using your two pipe wrenches,

1. unscrew the auger bucket end from the shaft
2. screw a coupling onto the shaft
3. screw on a new length of pipe
4. screw the auger bucket onto the extended shaft

Now you are ready to drill another 4 or 5 feet.

Repeat this procedure each time you need to until you finish drilling your well. By the time you're finished, your auger may use 4 or 5 additional lengths of pipe and be 30 feet long. And as it gets longer, it gets heavier. Not only do the extension pipes add to the weight, they also fill up with water up to the level of the water table while you are drilling. So lift the auger out <u>slowly</u> once you've dug below the water level and allow the water in the extension pipes to drain out. Allowing the water to drain out as you raise the auger slowly reduces the total weight of the auger considerably.

It's a good idea to drill a small ($1/8$-inch) air hole in the auger handle to let air enter and escape from the extension pipes as the auger is lowered into and raised from the hole. Remember to lift a full bucket out slowly so the diggings are not washed out of the bucket by water draining from the extension pipes.

Emptying a bucket at the end of a 30-foot long auger can be tricky. You don't want any high voltage wires overhead or bay windows nearby for you to put the auger handle through when you lift the auger out of the hole.

A 27-foot auger.

Also, as you add extension lengths of pipe to your auger, you'll notice something new about the digging process: TORQUE. If your auger encounters resistance in the form of embedded rocks, you'll be able to give a 30-foot auger almost a quarter-turn before the bucket will rotate at the other end. This isn't a problem - but it can be surprising if you're not expecting it.

Keep a permanent record of digging your well. A log form is contained in the Appendix. This record will be a valuable reference during the well's use and maintenance and in the event the well is to be deepened or abandoned.

When you strike water, you will notice that the material you withdraw in the auger bucket will change to more of a sand and gravel consistency. Keep digging.

After a while, you will probably see the material change to more of a clay consistency. This means you have dug through the water-bearing layer of sand and gravel and are now in a non-water-bearing layer. This may be time to quit digging.

If you keep digging, you may strike another, even better water-bearing layer. Or you may not.

It is very helpful at this point to have some local knowledge about other wells in the area. How deep are they?

Remember, once you stop digging and install the casing, it's very difficult to make the well any deeper if you change your mind. The water level in your well will go up and down with the seasons and the amount of rainfall you get. You want your well to be as deep as possible so you'll still have water when the water table drops during dry periods.

Drill an air hole in the auger handle.

Whenever you are not actually working on your well, make certain that it is covered and secure. Children, kittens and just about everyone is attracted to a hole in the ground. You don't want anything, or any<u>one</u> falling into your well. A good temporary cover (see illustration) includes properly sloping sides, plywood and a bag of concrete or other heavy material that children can't remove.

If you've hit water but find that you don't make any real progress after an hour or so of digging, you may have encountered an impervious layer that is trapping the water above it.

When you've reached the point that you just can't, or don't want to, go any deeper, its time to install the casing.

Cover the well securely between digging sessions.

SAMPLE DRILLER'S LOG.

— WELL OWNER —

Name ___John Wilson___

Mailing Address ___42 Scenic Drive___

___Ogden___ ___UT___ ___84401___
CITY   STATE   ZIP

— WELL LOCATION —

Address ___42 Scenic Drive___

City ___Ogden___

County _____

APN Book _____ Page _____ Parcel _____
   or
Township _____ Range _____ Section _____
   or
Latitude _____ NORTH   Longitude _____ WEST
    DEG.   MIN.   SEC.   DEG.   MIN.   SEC.

— LOCATION SKETCH —

NORTH

136 feet → well (X)

62 feet

House

Drive-way

Street

SOUTH

Illustrate or Describe Distance of Well from Landmarks such as Roads, Buildings, Fences, Rivers, etc.
PLEASE BE ACCURATE & COMPLETE.

— ACTIVITY (✓) —

✓ NEW WELL

MODIFICATION / REPAIR

___ Deepen

___ Other (Specify)

___ DESTROY *(Describe Procedures and Materials Under "GEOLOGIC LOG")*

PLANNED USE(S) (✓)
___ MONITORING

WATER SUPPLY

___ Domestic

___ Public

✓ Irrigation

___ Industrial

___ "TEST WELL"

___ CATHODIC PROTECTION

___ OTHER (Specify)

DRILLING METHOD ___Hand auger___ FLUID _____

— WATER LEVEL & YIELD OF COMPLETED WELL —

DEPTH OF STATIC WATER LEVEL ___14___ (Ft.) & DATE MEASURED _____

ESTIMATED YIELD* ___8___ (GPM) & TEST TYPE ___Free Flow Pump___

TEST LENGTH ___1/2___ (Hrs.) TOTAL DRAWDOWN ___4___ (Ft.)

* May not be representative of a well's long-term yield.

Date Work Began ___7/4/91___, Ended ___7/20/91___

GEOLOGIC LOG

ORIENTATION (✓) ✔ VERTICAL ____ HORIZONTAL ____ ANGLE ____ (SPECIFY)

DEPTH TO FIRST WATER __13__ (Ft.) BELOW SURFACE

DESCRIPTION

Describe material, grain size, color, etc.

DEPTH FROM SURFACE Ft. to Ft.	DESCRIPTION
O · 5	TOPSOIL few rocks
5 · 13	YELLOW & BROWN Clay & Sand
13 · 17	BROWN Sand & GRAVEL & WATER
17 · 22	THICK YELLOW/BROWN CLAY
·	
·	
·	
·	
·	
·	
·	
·	
·	

TOTAL DEPTH OF BORING __22__ (Feet)

TOTAL DEPTH OF COMPLETED WELL __21__ (Feet)

DEPTH FROM SURFACE Ft. to Ft.	BORE-HOLE DIA. (Inches)	CASING(S)			
		MATERIAL / GRADE	INTERNAL DIAMETER (Inches)	GAUGE OR WALL THICKNESS	SLOT SIZE IF ANY (Inches)
O · 21	9	White PVC	4	Sched. 40	⅛" X 2"
·					
·					

DEPTH FROM SURFACE Ft. to Ft.	ANNULAR MATERIAL			
	TYPE			
	CE-MENT (✓)	BEN-TONITE (✓)	FILL (✓)	FILTER PACK (TYPE/SIZE)
O · 11	✔			
11 · 22			✓	PEA GRAVEL
·				

33

THE WELL CASING

If you don't line the inside of the well with something, the walls will eventually collapse. The "casing" is the lining of the well. Thick-walled, Schedule 40 PVC white plastic irrigation pipe is an ideal casing which is easy to work with.

The casing pipe fits inside the hole you dig so its diameter has to be smaller than that of the hole. The space between the outside of the casing and the walls of the hole you dig is called the "annular" space. This annular space needs to be at least 2 inches[1] all around the casing; you will backfill this space with pea gravel at the bottom of the well and with concrete for the top 10 feet of the well.

A 4-inch diameter pipe is ideal for a hand-augered well. Most hand augers are about 7 inches across and generate a hole that ends up being about 9¼ inches across and that leaves just enough annular space. The bore hole can be made wider by using an adjustable auger.

For now, the length of the casing should be several feet longer than the depth of the well. When you're finished, the casing needs to be at least 12 inches above the pumphouse floor or final ground elevation and not less than 12 inches[2] above the normally anticipated flood level for your location.

---

[1] EPA Manual of Water Well Construction, pg. 85.

[2] EPA recommends at least 24 inches above highest known flood level.

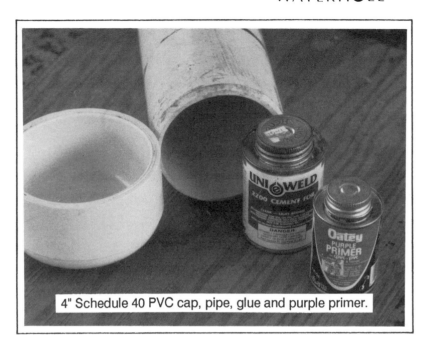

4" Schedule 40 PVC cap, pipe, glue and purple primer.

ANNULAR SPACE

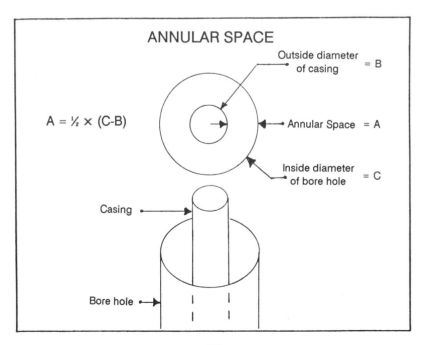

$A = \frac{1}{2} \times (C-B)$

Outside diameter of casing = B

Annular Space = A

Inside diameter of bore hole = C

Casing

Bore hole

Once you've finished digging the well, measure its depth several times with a weighted string. When you install the casing, it will stick up out of the ground. Later you'll trim the top of casing to the proper height - **but only after everything else is done.**

When you measure the depth of the well, also determine the standing water level, or high water mark, in the well. If the water fills the well up to a height 12 feet below ground level, then the high water mark is 12 feet. You'll want the slits in the casing to begin at this point and continue to the bottom of the well.

To allow water to enter the casing, cut slits across the pipe with a circular saw about **two** inches long and **1** inch apart. **Be sure to wear protective eyewear when cutting the slits!** Start 6 inches from the bottom end of the casing and stagger the slits around and up the length of the casing to the high water level. Use coarse sandpaper to remove any burrs you've made cutting slits in the casing.

After cleaning the casing thoroughly inside and out, glue one of the two caps to the **bottom end** (the end with the slits) of the casing. (All PVC pipe one inch in diameter or larger should receive a coat of purple primer before gluing. Allow the primer to dry before applying any glue.)

The bottom cap seals the end of the casing and helps keep silt from entering. It also ensures that anything you accidentally drop into the well stays inside the casing to facilitate retrieval.

Place, **don't glue,** the other cap on the top end of the casing. This will help keep foreign materials from getting into the casing as work continues.

Use a circular saw to cut 2" slits in the casing.

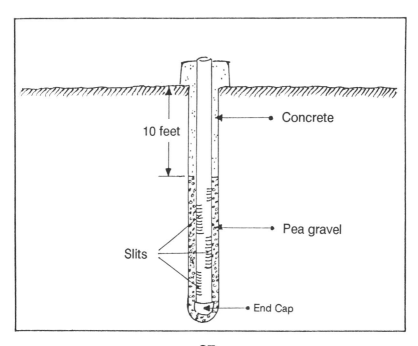

10 feet

Concrete

Pea gravel

Slits

End Cap

It's finally time to lower the casing into the well. This is a good time to have a friend help who can help lift and steady the casing as it is installed in the well.

First drop a couple shovels full of pea gravel into the well as a base for the casing. Next, <u>carefully</u> lower the casing (capped and slitted end first) into the well. Be careful not to rub against the sides of the well. Lower the casing all the way to the bottom until it rests on the pea gravel base.

Use a level to make sure the casing is plumb while centering it in the hole. Pour pea gravel in around the casing. Stop back-filling when the pea gravel gets to a level 10 feet below the surface (use your measuring stick to check this).

Now it's time to pour the concrete seal in the top 10 feet of the annular space.

Use a level to ensure the casing is plumb.

SEALING THE CASING

To seal the well against contamination, the top 10 feet (at least) of the space around the outside of the casing (the annular space) is filled with concrete. The concrete can also form a base for mounting the well cap and pump.

The annular space should be at least 2 inches on all sides of the casing[1].

The surface pad should slope away from the center of the casing in all directions. It should rise at least 4 inches above the ground and extend at least 10 feet below the surface. The required depth of the concrete seal depends on the depth of the well. Ten feet is sufficient for hand-augered wells.

Mix and pour all of the concrete during one session to eliminate any voids. A mixture of Portland Cement (ASTM C150), sand, coarse aggregate and water in the proportion of at least five (5) bags of cement per cubic yard of concrete to not more than seven (7) gallons of clean water per bag of cement (one cubic foot or 94 pounds) should be used.

When pouring the seal, pour the concrete around the casing evenly as the annular space fills up and be sure to keep the casing plumb and centered in the well. Be careful not to

---

[1] Water Well Construction Practices, EPA - 570/9-75-001.

Fill the annular space with concrete to a depth of 10 feet.

Remove the "collar" when the concrete fills to the surface.

disturb the sides of the well and avoid mixing any soil or other material into the concrete as you pour the seal.

You may wish to broaden and shape the portion of the seal that extends above the surface (minimum 4 inches) into a pad for your pump. Make a form for your pad out of scrap lumber or bender board at least 6 inches high. You can install mounting bolts into the wet concrete pad if you know how to space them for your pump. The surface of the pad should slope away from the center of the well.

The example in this guide uses an inverted 15-gallon plastic nursery container with the bottom cut off as a form for the surface pad. Once the concrete has hardened, the container is pried off with a crow bar and the concrete is finished with a stiff scrub brush.

Remember that the casing should extend at least 12 inches above the surface; you may wish to pour the concrete pad to that level as well. Once the concrete has set, cut the casing with a hand saw at least 1½" above the concrete seal. Allow the concrete to cure for at least 4 days before mounting the pump or using the well.

An inverted 15 gallon nursery container makes an idea form.

Cut the extra casing off with a hand saw.

CAPPING THE WELL

The top of the well must be sealed to prevent the entrance of foreign material. How the well is capped is referred to as its "surface construction features" or "termination."

A suitable cap can be made from a rubber gasket sandwiched between two circular plates. The plates can be metal or PVC and cut to fit the casing per the illustration. Three or more bolts pass through this "sandwich" to allow tightening and compression of the gasket so it expands beyond the sides of the plates to seal the well.

Openings into the top of the well which are designed to provide access to the well, i.e., for measuring, chlorinating, etc., should be protected against entrance of surface waters or foreign matter by installation of watertight caps or plugs[1].

Where the pump is installed directly over the casing, a watertight seal (gasket) should be placed between the pump head and the pump base, or a watertight seal (gasket) should be placed between the pump base and the rim of the casing.

Where the pump is offset from the well or where a submersible pump is used, the opening between the well casing and any pipes or cables which enter the well should be closed with a watertight seal or well cap.

---

[1] Bulletin 74-81, Water Well Standards, California, 1981.

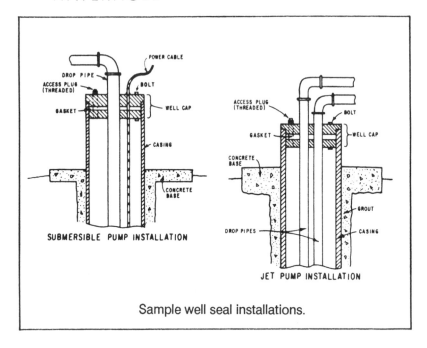

POWER CABLE

DROP PIPE

ACCESS PLUG
(THREADED)

BOLT

GASKET

WELL CAP

CASING

CONCRETE
BASE

SUBMERSIBLE PUMP INSTALLATION

ACCESS PLUG
(THREADED)

BOLT

GASKET

WELL CAP

CONCRETE
BASE

GROUT

DROP PIPES

CASING

JET PUMP INSTALLATION

Sample well seal installations.

A temporary cap is used until the pump is installed.

If the pump is not installed immediately or if there is a prolonged interruption in construction of the well, a watertight cover should be installed at the top of the well.

If a concrete base or slab (sometimes called a pump block or pedestal) is constructed around the casing, it should be free from cracks, honeycombs or other defects likely to detract from its watertightness. The joint between the base and the annular seal must also be watertight. The base should slope away from the well casing. The minimum thickness of the concrete base should be 4 inches.

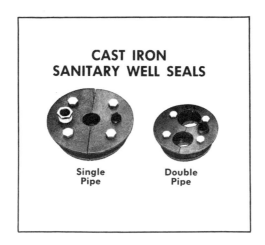

**CAST IRON
SANITARY WELL SEALS**

Single
Pipe

Double
Pipe

THE PUMP

The pump you select should match:

1. the Well
2. the Use

Matching the Well: The water pumping level and capacity of your well should match the specifications of your pump. If your water pumping level is 12 feet, you need a pump that will lift water at least 12 feet. And if your well's capacity is 200 gallons per hour (gph), your pump should deliver a little less than 200 gph so it doesn't pump the well dry before it can recover.

A higher capacity pump can be throttled back by using a partially closed valve on the output side of the pump, but this is not ideal.

How to determine the capacity and water pumping level is explained later in this section.

Matching the Use: After matching the well's specifications for lift and delivery rate, consider your use of the water. If it will be pumped into a storage tank for later use, the pumping rate is not as critical as if the water is to be pumped directly into a high pressure sprinkling system. If you are pumping up into a storage tank that's eight feet high, you need a pump that will pump above an eight foot head.

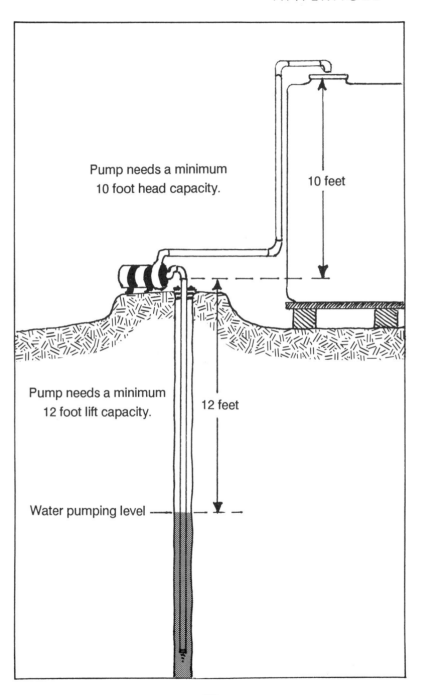

Pump needs a minimum
10 foot head capacity.

10 feet

Pump needs a minimum
12 foot lift capacity.

12 feet

Water pumping level

47

There are four basic types of well pumps in use today. They are distinguished by their pumping mechanisms:

> Piston
> Single-drop pipe jet
> Double-drop pipe jet
> Submersible

Piston

Few piston pumps have been installed in recent years. The piston pump is a suction device where water is drawn into a cylinder by means of a moving piston which is fitted with leather seals. Many of these types of pumps are powered by windmills or the classic hand-operated pitcher pump.

A rod is connected to the piston and extends up through the well casing to the power source. The water in the piston is held in place by a check valve while another stroke pulls more water into the cylinder and up the riser pipe. With each stroke, more water is raised until it reaches the top of the riser pipe and spills out at the surface. In this example the piston is submerged in the well casing but may also be located at the surface.

Piston pumps, though simple and reliable, are comparatively inefficient and slow. Unless you have a special reason for choosing one, a jet or submersible pump would be a better choice.

Single-drop pipe jet

Jet pumps are suction pumps located at the surface of the well and therefore are only capable of operating from shal-

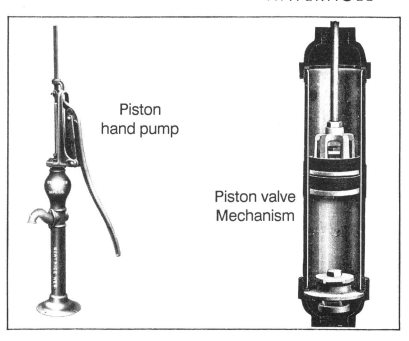

Piston
hand pump

Piston valve
Mechanism

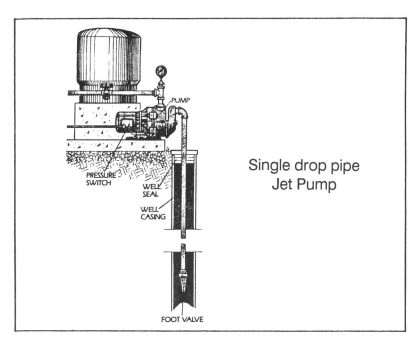

PUMP

PRESSURE
SWITCH

WELL
SEAL

WELL
CASING

FOOT VALVE

Single drop pipe
Jet Pump

49

low wells (such as your hand-augered well). They require a continuous prime to operate so the drop pipe and pump cavity must be full of water to pull up more water. This prime is maintained by a foot valve at the bottom of the drop pipe.

When the pump is turned on, impellers in the pump push water out while drawing new water up behind the prime water. A restricting device called an ejector boosts the velocity of the water as it passes through the pump and creates a continuous vacuum that increases the power of the pump. The ejector is located at the pump.

A single-drop pipe pump is probably the least expensive choice for pumping from your 20- to 30-foot well and will do a good job. They are not recommended for wells much beyond 30 feet in depth.

If you can afford to spend more, you may wish to consider either of the next two types of pumps.

Double-drop pipe jet ————————————————————

While similar to the single-drop version, the double-drop pipe pump has its ejector located at the bottom of the well and connects the two drop pipes. Once water reaches the pump through the suction pipe, a portion is diverted to the second pipe and drops down to the ejector. It passes through the ejector, creating even greater lift in the suction pipe.

A double-drop pipe pump will be more expensive but can lift water from as much as 120 feet deep, compared to the single-drop system's lift of about 30 feet.

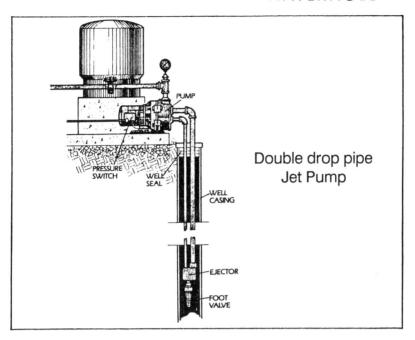

PUMP

PRESSURE
SWITCH

WELL
SEAL

WELL
CASING

Double drop pipe
Jet Pump

EJECTOR

FOOT
VALVE

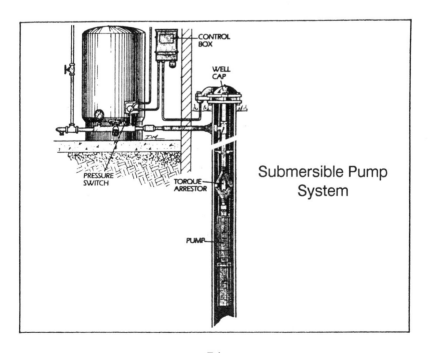

CONTROL
BOX

WELL
CAP

PRESSURE
SWITCH

TORQUE
ARRESTOR

PUMP

Submersible Pump
System

Submersible

Submersible pumps are suspended in the casing, directly in the aquifer. A sealed electrical motor powers an impeller which simply forces water up the single drop pipe to the surface.

Generally considered the most problem-free, submersible pumps are typically the most expensive and have a major drawback: You have to hire a professional with equipment to retrieve and service the pump. This process is called "pulling the well" and can be expensive and disruptive to surrounding landscaping.

Submersible pumps are frequently used in deep wells where neither piston nor jet pumps can provide enough lifting power. Submersibles are probably an overkill for your hand-augered well.

About Pumps

Pumps are rated at gallons per minute and should be matched to your well's recovery rate since you can't pump water out faster than the well can supply it. The recovery rate is difficult to estimate until you start pumping water from the well.

A small sprinkler needs about 8 gallons per minute to operate. You might consider this the minimum acceptable output without a water storage tank. If you will have some form of a storage tank, then even a much slower output can be acceptable since the water can continue to accumulate indefinitely (see WATER STORAGE section). Automatic shut-off switches may be installed on the pump to sense

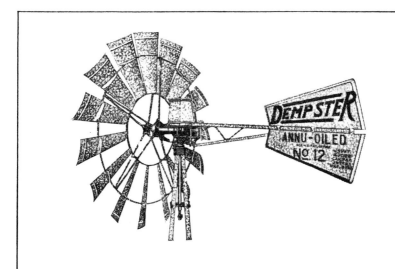

Windmills are well-suited for piston pumping.

Attach pump with a union (for easy disconnect), screen and seal.

when the tank is full or when the water level in the well has dropped too low. This allows a totally automated water supply system.

No matter how slowly your well produces, you can have a continuous or timed pump fill a storage tank which holds a large volume of water. Any overflow can be directed right back into the well.

At the bottom of the well, the end of the hose should have some sort of screen or filter so the pump won't "inhale" material which will damage it. The depth of the well should be determined with a weighted string and the hose cut about 6" shorter so it doesn't rest on the bottom. Check the depth from time to time as sediment can gather and should be removed (see maintenance section).

Well Capacity

You can determine how much water your well produces in gallons per minute by running a "clean-out" pump (preferably an old pump) for 30 minutes at free (wide open) flow. After 30 minutes, time how long it takes to fill a 5-gallon bucket and plug that time (in seconds) into this formula to get a gallons per hour figure:

$$18,000 \div \text{(time in seconds)} = \text{gallons per hour}$$

If water stops flowing at any time during the 30 minutes, turn the pump off immediately. After waiting 4 hours, lower the pump deeper into the well and throttle back the pump by using a gate valve on the output side of the pump and closing it ¼-turn. This procedure should be repeated until the pump can flow continuously for 30 minutes.

Final installation of well dug for this guide. Note plug at left for priming, well seal, union and pipe supports.

Submersible pump installation. Rope is for pump retrieval.

Water Pumping Level

To determine the water pumping level, add 1.) the total vertical feet from the highest outlet to ground level to 2.) the total vertical feet from ground level to the pumping level of the water. This is the standing water level in the well when the pump is operating and the water being pumped out equals the water entering the well. This is normally several feet lower than the water level in the well when the pump is not operating.

The water pumping level determines pump performance, not how deep the pump is placed below this level.

Remember that almost every new well increases its capacity and production after prolonged pumping. Pumping cleans out and broadens the water veins leading to your well.

In contrast, wells that allowed to sit unused for prolonged periods, will become clogged with silt. They will then need to be flushed and pumped out to renew their productivity.

Use your well frequently.

DISINFECTION

Before the well is placed in service, it must be disinfected. For wells drilled by hand auger with a 4-inch casing and a depth of about 20 feet, add 10 ounces of regular (5.25%) laundry-variety chlorine bleach (like Purex or Clorox) to the well.

After pouring it into the well, add potable water in an amount at least equal to the amount that had been standing in the well. This back-flushing will force the disinfectant out through the casing into the annular space. Let the well sit for at least 12 hours.

Note: Where water has a low pH, special care should be taken due to the highly corrosive nature of a chlorine solution having a low pH. You can test the pH of your water with test paper available at your drug store.

After the 12-hour (minimum) contact period, pump the well to clear it of the disinfectant. Dispose of the purged water so as to avoid damage to vegetation or aquatic life.

During the construction of the well, the tools and work site should be kept clean and free from contaminants. Clean the site thoroughly upon completion of the well. Grease, oil, soil and other foreign substances can harbor bacteria and hide it from subsequent disinfection attempts. So keep the work area clean and keep anything from falling into the well.

WATER STORAGE

You may simply want to pump water as you use it.

However, without a means of storing it, the amount of water you can access at any time is limited to the volume the pump can deliver within the limitations of your well's recovery rate. It also means turning the pump on and off every time you draw water, no matter how little you need.

For these and other reasons, most well-owners have some sort of water storage capacity. It can be as simple as a raised tank that can then deliver water by gravity, or it can be one of the more convenient pressurized tank and switch systems which are common to most wells.

The pressure tank is normally a galvanized steel tank with a pressure switch threaded into it which operates the pump according to how much water is in the tank. The tank is partially filled with air which becomes compressed when water is pumped into the tank. The compressed air forces the water out when you open a faucet.

The pressure switch can be set to turn the pump on at one pressure (e.g. 25 psi) and turn it off at another (e.g. 45 psi). Therefore the pump is not activated each time a little water is used, but only after a substantial amount is drawn. This saves wear and tear on the pump as well as eliminating wide fluctuations in water pressure at the faucet.

Non-pressurized storage tanks are frequently made of poly-ethylene. They may be buried or surface mounted. They vary in size from 65 gallons to 10,000 gallons from the supplier listed in the Appendix.

Cost for a good quality tank averages about 50¢ per gallon and ranges from about 39¢/gal. to about 80¢/gal. depending on style and manufacturer. Some sizes are more popular than others for domestic use and therefore are priced at a lower cost per gallon than less popular models. Ask for the best selling models for the best value.

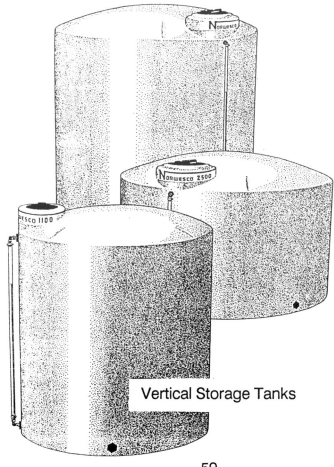

Vertical Storage Tanks

MAINTENANCE

A well doesn't need a lot of maintenance. But there are a few things you should do to make sure you don't have any problems:

Maintaining the Pump ————————————————

If you are using a hand pump, it's a good idea to pump a little water from it at least every couple weeks to keep moving parts working. Add some grease or oil to moving parts where wear occurs.

If you have an electric pump, it's also a good idea to run it every couple of weeks. Most pumps today are self-lubricating and so you won't need to worry about oil or grease. Follow the manufacturer's recommended maintenance schedule.

Maintaining the Well ————————————————

Keep the well site clear of vegetation and debris for a radius of at least four feet. Keep the well cap closed and secure. Don't store anything that could contaminate the well, particularly liquid, nearby. Things have a way of finding their way into the well.

It's a good idea to check the surface construction (well head, pump pad, etc.) periodically for cracks in the concrete which may allow surface fluids to enter the well. Repair any cracks with concrete patching compound.

Don't "store" extra water (e.g. from your swimming pool) in your well. This contaminates the ground water.

Your well may accumulate silt at the bottom from too little use or for other reasons. Removing the silt is basically a matter of stirring it up and pumping it out. This involves backflushing with potable water under pressure and pumping the water and silt out. Once the well has been in use for a few weeks, silt shouldn't be a problem if the well is used at least once a week.

Jet Pump with "Captive Air" pressurized storage tank.

ABANDONMENT

Digging a well carries with it the responsibility of returning the ground to its original state should the well or test hole ever be abandoned. Nobody digs a well thinking they'll ever abandon it, but circumstances change and you may have to.

If that time comes, you need to fill at least the top 20 feet of the well or bore hole with concrete. The space below the top 20 feet may be filled with clay, silt, sand, gravel, crushed stone or native soils.

The basic concept behind proper sealing or "destroying" abandoned wells is the restoration of the geohydrologic conditions that existed before the well was drilled and constructed. An improperly abandoned well may serve as an invasion point for contaminated and polluted water.

To seal a well properly, several things must be accomplished:

1. elimination of the physical hazard
2. prevention of ground water contamination
3. conservation of yield of the aquifer
4. prevention of intermingling of desirable and undesirable waters

The sealing process for abandonment applies to unsuccessful bore holes as well as successful holes.

Sealing an Abandoned Well

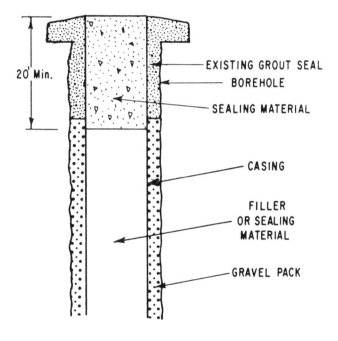

20' Min.

EXISTING GROUT SEAL
BOREHOLE
SEALING MATERIAL

CASING

FILLER
OR SEALING
MATERIAL

GRAVEL PACK

The top 20 feet are filled with concrete.

GLOSSARY

ABANDONED WELL - a well not used for a period of one year, unless the owner demonstrates his intention to use the well again.

ANNULAR SPACE - the space between the casing and the wall of the drilled hole.

AQUIFER - water-bearing layer of permeable rock, sand or gravel.

AUGER - tool for drilling wells. May be hand, gas or hydraulic powered.

BACKFILL - material (like pea gravel) that is used to fill back around the outside of the well casing.

CASING - a tubular retaining structure (a pipe) that is installed in the well bore to maintain the well opening.

COLLAR - a 10- to 12-inch diameter ring about 12 inches high that is placed at the top of the well hole to keep loose material from falling back into the hole during construction.

DIVINING ROD - a forked rod believed to indicate the presence of water by dipping downward when held over a vein.

DOWSE - to search for underground water or minerals by using a divining rod.

G.P.M. - gallons per minute is a measurement of the rate of flow (like water pumped from a well).

GROUND WATER - water within the earth that supplies wells and springs; water in the part of the ground that is wholly saturated.

POTABLE - a liquid that is suitable for drinking.

JET PUMP - one type of surface-mounted water pump.

RECOVERY RATE - a measurement (usually in gallons per minute) of how quickly a well refills itself as water is removed.

SEAL - a concrete barrier at least 10 feet deep around the top of the well casing that keeps surface water and other contaminants from entering the well and polluting the ground water.

SILT - fine soil that can clog a well.

SUBMERSIBLE PUMP - a type of pump (usually long and thin) that is placed at the bottom of the well shaft.

WATER TABLE - underground water stored in the soil (usually refers to the water level, i.e. how deep below the surface does water exist).

BIBLIOGRAPHY

Drilling For Water. (Interview) by Bob Freudenberger, Home Mechanix, November 1988.

Ground Water and Wells. Fletcher G. Driscoll. Johnson Division, Universal Oil Products., Second Edition, 1986.

Ground Water Hydrology for Water Well Contractors. Stuart Smith, et al, ed. NWWA[1], Revised, 1982.

Grouting and Abandoning Water Wells. Anthology of eleven articles. NWWA[1]

How to Troubleshoot a Water Well. Merle Henkenius and Don Mannes, Popular Mechanics, Sept. 1989.

Manual of Water Well Construction Practices – **EPA-570/9-75-001**, United States Environmental Protection Agency, Office of Water Supply.

Planning for an Individual Water System. American Association for Vocational Instructional Materials, Athens, GA, Fourth Edition, 1982.

Protecting Your Rural Well: Turning the Tide on Ground Water Contamination. Letitia Savage, Country Journal, Sept.- Oct. 1989.

Report Offers Hope of Curbing Well Water Woes. Successful Farming, January 1991.

Rural Living Handbook. Mother Earth News Partners, Fireside/Simon & Schuster, 1989.

Water Rights in California. State Water Resources Control Board, Sacramento, CA, 1990.

Water Systems Handbook. Water Systems Council, 221 No. LaSalle, Suite 2026, Chicago, IL.

Water Wells and Pumps: Their Design, Construction, Operation and Maintenance. V.H. Scott and J.C. Scalmanini. ANR Publications (Bulletin 1889), University of California, 6701 San Pablo, Oakland, CA.

Water Well Standards: State of California, Bulletin 74-81. State of California, Department of Water Resources.

Well Drilling Manual. Speedstar Division, Koehring Co., NWWA[1] Catalog #47.

---

[1] National Water Well Association, 6375 Riverside Drive, Dublin Ohio 43017.

APPENDIX

Environmental Agencies

United States Environmental Protection Agency, Office of Water Supply, 401 M Street S.W., Washington, D.C. 20460.

California Department of Water Resources, Box 942836, Sacramento, CA 94236-0001.

Trade Associations

National Water Well Association, 6375 Riverside Drive, Dublin OH 43017.

Water Testing

County Department of Health and Human Services.

Municipal Water District.

Pumps & Equipment

Water Tank Distributors, In CA: 1-800-655-9100. Outside CA: 1-707-882-2422.

Forster Pump & Engineering Company, 56 Woodland Avenue, San Rafael, CA 94901 (415) 459-4770.

Grainger Equipment & Supplies, (Pumps) 1-800-323-0620.

The Natural Gardening Company, (Augers) 217 San Anselmo Avenue, San Anselmo, CA 94960 (415) 456-5060.

Northern Hydraulics, (Pumps) 1-800-533-5545.

Well Driller's Log

—— WELL OWNER ——

Name _____

Mailing Address _____

CITY _____ STATE ___ ZIP ___

—— WELL LOCATION ——

Address _____

City _____

County _____

APN Book _____ Page _____ Parcel _____
or
Township _____ Range _____ Section _____
or
Latitude ___|___|___ NORTH Longitude ___|___|___ WEST
       DEG. MIN. SEC.   DEG. MIN. SEC.

—— LOCATION SKETCH ——

NORTH

WEST   EAST

SOUTH

Illustrate or Describe Distance of Well from Landmarks such as Roads, Buildings, Fences, Rivers, etc.
PLEASE BE ACCURATE & COMPLETE.

ACTIVITY (✓)

___ NEW WELL

MODIFICATION/REPAIR

___ Deepen

___ Other (Specify)

___ DESTROY *(Describe Procedures and Materials Under "GEOLOGIC LOG")*

PLANNED USE(S) (✓)

___ MONITORING

WATER SUPPLY

___ Domestic

___ Public

___ Irrigation

___ Industrial

___ "TEST WELL"

___ CATHODIC PROTECTION

___ OTHER (Specify)

DRILLING METHOD _____ FLUID _____

—— WATER LEVEL & YIELD OF COMPLETED WELL ——

DEPTH OF STATIC WATER LEVEL _____ (Ft.) & DATE MEASURED _____

ESTIMATED YIELD* _____ (GPM) & TEST TYPE _____

TEST LENGTH _____ (Hrs.) TOTAL DRAWDOWN _____ (Ft.)

* May not be representative of a well's long-term yield.

Date Work Began _____ , Ended _____

— WATERHOLE —

— GEOLOGIC LOG —

ORIENTATION (∠) _____ VERTICAL _____ HORIZONTAL _____ ANGLE _____ (SPECIFY)

DEPTH TO FIRST WATER _____ (Ft.) BELOW SURFACE

DEPTH FROM SURFACE		DESCRIPTION
Ft.	to Ft.	*Describe material, grain size, color, etc.*

TOTAL DEPTH OF BORING _____ (Feet)

TOTAL DEPTH OF COMPLETED WELL _____ (Feet)

DEPTH FROM SURFACE		BORE-HOLE DIA. (Inches)	CASING(S)			
Ft.	to Ft.		MATERIAL/ GRADE	INTERNAL DIAMETER (Inches)	GAUGE OR WALL THICKNESS	SLOT SIZE IF ANY (Inches)

DEPTH FROM SURFACE		ANNULAR MATERIAL			
		TYPE			
Ft.	to Ft.	CE-MENT (∠)	BEN-TONITE (∠)	FILL (∠)	FILTER PACK (TYPE/SIZE)

70

CAN YOU DIG IT?

The colorful **WATERHOLE T-Shirt** is popular with well diggers.
See the form on the next page to order yours.

—WATERHOLE—

ORDER FORM

PHONE ORDERS
415-453-8886
Mon-Fri 8am-4pm

FAX ORDERS
415-453-8888
24 hours a day

MAIL ORDERS
11 Library Place
San Anselmo
CA 94960

FAX OR PHONE ORDERS FOR SAME-DAY SHIPPING

Qty	Item#	Description	Cost	Amount
	801	HAND AUGER — 6" w/ hard maple handle (add $9. shipping per auger)	$48.	
	802	WATERHOLE T-Shirt — S, M, L, XL (add $3. shipping per shirt)	12.	
	803	DIVINING ROD — hand-finished wood (add $3. shipping per rod) NOT GUARANTEED.	8.	

Shipping	
Subtotal	
CA Residents Sales Tax	
TOTAL ENCLOSED:	

WATERHOLE Book
Quantity discounts available.
Call for prices.
415-453-8886

METHOD OF PAYMENT:

☐ CHECK (Payable to BALBOA PUBLISHING)

☐ Purchase Order # _____

☐ MasterCard   ☐ VISA   Exp. Date _____/_____

   Card # _____

SHIP TO:

Name: _____

Street (No P.O. Boxes): _____

City: _____ State: _____ Zip: _____

BALBOA PUBLISHING CORPORATION, 11 Library Place, San Anselmo, CA 94960